Printed and Published by D. C. Thomson & Co., Ltd.,
Dundee and London

Hi, Girls,

I'm sure you're going to enjoy this super new **Twinkle Book** that's specially for you.

The invisible princess, Miranda's mirror and **Patty and the Grisly Gripe** are just some of the great stories inside.

You'll find lots of puzzles to do and two exciting games to play!

Plus — **Nurse Nancy, Patch, Silly Milly, Penny Crayon, Sam** and all your favourite **Twinkle** chums in **64** fun-packed pages.

Love,
Twinkle.

Nurse Nancy

1 — It was almost tea-time at the Dollies Hospital. Nurse Nancy was just putting a sick teddy to bed before feeding the other patients, when Melanie Trent came in.

2 — Melanie was carrying a doll which had loose stitching. "That's a very old doll," said Nancy. "I got her at a jumble sale," Melanie told her.

3 — Mr Jingle inspected the doll who was called Louise. "She's a very special doll," he told Melanie, "but she needs quite a bit of work."

4 — Grandad asked Melanie to leave Louise. He started work using a pair of dainty tweezers. Nancy had never seen a doll handled so delicately before. "This doll is very valuable," said Grandad.

5 — After a lot of careful work, the doll was restored. Nancy tried to find some clothes for her. "Modern clothes don't look right," said Nancy.

6 — Together with Colin, the ambulance boy, Nancy went to the library. They looked at books about dolls' costumes. "That dress would suit Louise perfectly," said Nancy.

7 — The little nurse borrowed the book, then set about copying the dress in the picture. She started at the sewing shop. "Here's some nice lace," she thought.

8 — Nancy also found a piece of velvet which wasn't expensive, then hurried back to the hospital to cut out the costume. She cleverly added extra touches of her own.

9 — Later, Nancy called Melanie to come and collect her antique doll. Melanie could hardly believe her eyes. "She's beautiful!" gasped the girl.

10 — A few days later, Mr Jingle was reading his newspaper when Nancy noticed an advert in it for an antique toy fair. "I wonder if Melanie would be interested in this?" she cried.

11 — Mr Jingle phoned Melanie right away. And so, when Nancy and Colin went to the antique fair, Louise looked splendid in the display — thanks to the hard work of Nurse Nancy and Mr Jingle!

Patch

Can you find eight butterflies hidden on these pages?

1 — One wet day, Paula Perkins cleaned out her toybox. "You can help, Patch," she told her kitten.

5 — As Paula strung the flowers together, Mummy suggested making beach posters. She helped Paula to draw some palm trees and the sun shining down on the sea.

2 — Soon, Paula heard a rustling sound. "You have found the paper flowers I wore when my class did a Hawaiian dance," she laughed.

3 — Then Paula found her grass skirt. "Let's have a Hawaiian party," she cried.

4 — Mummy agreed so Paula got busy making new flowers while Patch chased the old ones.

6 — Soon Paula's friends arrived with their Hawaiian costumes. "It's like Hawaii in here," the girls laughed as they danced. "Yes, we're having a lovely day, thanks to Patch," chuckled Paula. And the kitten purred proudly.

Winter fun-time

Lead Patsy, Buzzy and Carrie to the ski slopes.

Match the numbers to fill in the squares of this crossword.

Find six differences between these two pictures of Patsy and her chums enjoying themselves on their sledge.

ANSWERS —

1. (across) CAT 2. (down) CARROT 2. TORTOISE 3. BOAT 4. FLOAT 5. TRAIN 6. RABBIT 7. PHOTO 8. HEN 9. SNAKE 10. KITE 11. PARROT 12. TIGER 13. BIKE

Sam

SHONA MACGREGOR has a clever sheepdog called Sam. They live on a farm in the Scottish Highlands.

It had been snowing for several days and the conditions were perfect for one of the area's main winter attractions — the annual dog sleigh race.

Mr MacGregor and Shona went every year and, naturally, so did Sam. He loved to watch the huskies race around the wooded circuit, pulling the sleighs behind them.

"Who do you think will win this year?" Shona asked her father as the sleighs flashed by.

"Well, Jim McEwan, just passing us now, has a very good team," replied Mr MacGregor.

"Sam certainly seems to like them," chuckled Shona. "He's barked at them every time they've gone by, as if he's cheering them on!"

To prove her point, Sam gave an excited "wuff" — and the sheepdog's choice was a good one, for they did indeed win the race.

2 — As the MacGregors drove home afterwards, it began snowing heavily once more and even the farm truck found the going hard as the snow became deeper and deeper.

Shona became worried they'd *never* get home.

3 — It was a happy and relieved Shona who eventually sat in front of a blazing fire, sipping a mug of cocoa.

"I thought for a while we were going to be *stuck* in the snow," she shivered. "I'm glad we got home safely."

She was even happier the following morning, because all the roads were closed.

"Yippee!" she cried. "The school bus can't get through, so today's a holiday."

She fetched her sledge from the shed and spent the morning speeding down the slopes around the farm. Sam enjoyed this, too, and he raced alongside Shona, barking with pleasure.

Mr MacGregor, however, had more serious matters on his mind.

"The cottages on the far side of the loch will be completely cut off," he frowned. "They'll need supplies till the road is cleared."

4 — Mr MacGregor loaded a trailer with provisions and set off in his tractor to deliver them. But he didn't get very far before even the tractor's giant wheels began slipping and sliding in the snow.

"It's no use," he sighed. "The snow is going to be far too deep for me to get there."

Sam had an idea of his own, though! He stood by Shona's sledge and began barking.

5 — "Are you trying to tell us *you'd* pull the sledge?" laughed Shona. "We'd need a team of huskies to do that!"

Sam turned and raced away, leaving Shona and Mr MacGregor wondering what he was up to.

They soon found out, for, half an hour later, the sheepdog returned with several of the neighbourhood dogs.

"Sam's brought us his own dog team," gasped Shona. "Let's fix up a line to the sledge for them to pull."

And, in next to no time, Shona was ready to set off on her mercy mission, with the dogs pulling the sledge, laden with emergency supplies.

They skimmed over the surface of the snow, visiting all the farmfolk who were stranded in their cottages. Shona made sure that everyone had enough to last them and she promised to return every day till the snow was cleared.

6 — Shona *did* enjoy herself — almost as much as Sam. Jim McEwan's huskies might have won the dog sleigh race, but they were no match for the clever sheepdog and his doggy chums at delivering the goods!

"Perhaps we should enter *you* in the dog sleigh race next year," chuckled Shona. "I'm sure you'd win that, too!"

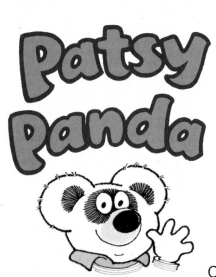

Patsy Panda

Oh, dear! My mice chums did *so* want to visit the adventure park.

Never mind — we'll go *here* instead.

Kind Mr Pipe, the plumber, can build . . .

. . . a super adventure ride with old pieces of piping! Have fun, chums!

Snow time

WHEN the wintry north winds blow,
Bringing crispy, crunchy snow,
I'll wrap up warm and run outside,
To make a shiny, slippery slide.

I'll build a snowman, big and fat,
With a carrot nose and Dad's old hat.
His eyes will be all shiny and bright,
To twinkle with the stars at night.

With a spade I'll clear the path,
And give the birds a fresh, clean bath.
I'll give them nuts and things to eat,
And some nice fruit cake for a treat.

I'll play at snowballs with my chum,
And do some shopping for my mum.
I'll slide downhill on an old tin tray,
And stay out in the snow all day.

And when I go to bed at night,
I'll call to my snowman, shiny and white,
"See you tomorrow. Please don't go away.
We've lots more wonderful games to play."

While Milly's mum is ill in bed —

Silly Milly

1 — Silly Milly is always in trouble. No matter what she does, it ends in a muddle. A few days before Christmas, Milly's mum had to take to her bed. Milly volunteered to do all the chores.

2 — There was lots to be done. Mum had baked a cake, but hadn't iced it yet. "I'll tackle that," smiled our chum. "I've seen Mum do it often enough." Meanwhile, Dad was busy plastering.

3 — Milly mixed what she thought was icing sugar and made a lovely job of the cake. However, it wouldn't cut. "You've used my plaster mix!" cried Dad. "What a mix-up!"

4 — The Christmas tree still needed decorating, so Milly did that job next. The tree soon looked really pretty with the tinsel and baubles. "All it needs now is the fairy on the top," thought Milly.

Our chum does all the chores instead!

5 — She needed a ladder to reach the top. Our chum leaned over to put the fairy in place, then the ladder wobbled. Milly stuck out her hand to steady herself — and pulled the tree down!

6 — On Christmas Day, Milly felt it was up to her to cook the meal. "Now, where's the turkey?" she wondered, opening the fridge. But there was no food inside. "Oh, no!" she exclaimed.

7 — However, she didn't have to worry as there was a nice surprise in store for her. Dad had booked a table at a posh restaurant for the three of them. "How lovely," said Mum who was better.

8 — "This is a reward for all the hard work you've put in," Dad told Milly, "even if things didn't always work out the way they should!" "Merry Christmas!" cried Milly, feeling proud.

The invisible princess

1 — Princess Rose was bored. "I'll go and see Mervin," she thought. Mervin was the magician who lived high in the castle turret.

2 — But Mervin wasn't in his workshop. "What's this?" asked Rose, looking at the magician's book of spells which lay open.

3 — "A vanishing spell!" she giggled. "I'll try it out." The princess repeated the words.

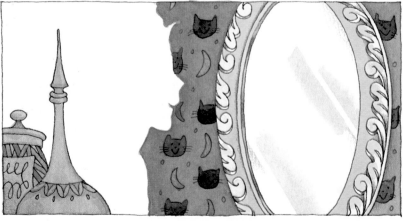

4 — In a puff of smoke, Princess Rose disappeared! She looked in a mirror and there was no reflection. "The spell really worked!" gasped Rose. "Now to have some fun."

5 — Rose gave her sister a push on the garden swing. "Who's there?" squeaked Poppy.

6 — Then the invisible princess ran off to the dining room. Rose mischievously lifted her father's crown off his head while he was eating. "Help!" he cried.

7 — In the kitchen, Rose took a newly-baked jam tart off the tray. "There's a ghost in my kitchen!" shrieked the shocked cook.

8 — She hurried off to tell the king. "I think we need Mervin's help with this invisible menace," said the king, leading the way.

9 — Just then, Mervin heard Rose giggle. "I think Princess Rose has been up to mischief," he frowned.

10 — "I don't want Mervin to make me reappear," thought Rose. She flew out the door, and straight into a painter's ladder!

11 — *CRASH!* A pot of paint fell over the princess and made her visible again! "Here she is!" everyone cried.

12 — Rose was covered in paint from head to toe and had to be scrubbed clean. "No more spells for me," she grumbled.

Cuddles and Co.

1 — Nadia has *lots* of pets. When Daddy set up her trampoline in the garden, the pets wanted to join in, too. "That looks fun," yapped Cuddles.

2 — But when the pets tried trampolining — disaster! "I can see stars," miaowed Tiny the kitten as their three heads collided. "And I feel giddy," moaned Midge the cat.

3 — Later, Nadia put her doll in the basket on her bike. "Let's go for a run," she said. Cuddles wagged his tail and the cats looked forward to it, too.

4 — Soon, however, Cuddles and the cats collapsed in a heap, exhausted. "I can't go any further," panted Cuddles. "Nor me," purred Tiny. Midge was too tired to speak.

5 — In the afternoon, Nadia played in the sandpit. Snowball the rabbit leapt in beside her and then Cuddles tried to bury his bone, leaving no room for the cats.

6 — Nadia's next game was *hairdressing* ! The pets didn't want to join in *that,* especially when Midge cried, "Ow!" Cuddles and Tiny ran off!

7 — But one game the pets *did* enjoy was *picnicking* ! They sat beside Nadia's dolls and waited for Nadia to pour some water and milk from her dolls' tea-set!

8 — Then there were carrots for Snowball, chocolate bones for Cuddles and biscuits for the cats. "I knew you would join in *this* game," laughed Nadia.

On the trail of Jenny Giraffe

An activity story

LITTLE Jenny Giraffe was lost. At once, all the other animals gathered together.

"What is she wearing?" asked PC Python.

"Well, her throat's sore so she was wearing a red scarf to keep her neck cosy," explained her mummy.

"We'll send out a search party," suggested PC Python.

"But where will we start?" asked Mrs Giraffe.

2 — Just then, Tina the tiger cub noticed red wool in a tree.

"It's from Jenny's scarf," cried Mrs Giraffe. "It must have caught in the branches."

"Then all we have to do is follow the trail of wool!" beamed PC Python.

You can search for Jenny Giraffe, too! Thread a length of red wool (about 160 cms) through a bodkin and knot one end. Then, starting at 1, push the bodkin in and out of the page following the trail of wool exactly. Tie a knot when you reach 34.

3 — Charlie Cheetah raced off and, when the others caught up with him, he was staring into a pool.

"The wool disappears here," he sighed. "Jenny must have had a drink."

Suddenly, Percy Parakeet squawked, "Here's the wool! Here's the wool!"

4 — "But where is it going now?" asked Jenny's mummy as the wool rose from the pool and disappeared around a hollow tree trunk.

PC Python slithered round and tracked down the trail again. It was leading to the bridge over the river.

5 — "We'll have to cross the river," Charlie told the others, taking the lead.

Soon Charlie held up his hand and told the others to stop.

"Shhh!" he whispered, and he pointed to some long grass.

There, lots of rabbits were having great fun, bobbing about and tangling the strand of wool *everywhere*!

"Leave this to me," ordered PC Python, and he stealthily crept along the ground towards the little animals.

Mrs Giraffe watched anxiously, hoping that the rabbits hadn't broken Jenny's trail.

6 — Just as PC Python was about to chase off the mischievous scamps, however, they saw the slithery snake approaching and a cheeky squirrel snatched the wool and scurried up a big tree.

Then the birds joined in, darting in and out.

7 — Mrs Giraffe and her friends waited down below while Minnie and Morris, the monkeys, gave chase. When the wool was dropped by a bird, Suki Squirrel picked it up again and playfully passed it to the other squirrels.

8 — "Stop! Stop!" ordered PC Python, but the silly squirrels thought it was all a game — especially when Morris and Minnie chased them.

At last, Minnie caught the squirrel who had the wool and she passed it to PC Python who had crept close by.

PC Python followed the trail — and what do you think he found?

9 — He found Jenny Giraffe! There she was, standing behind the tree!

Have *you* found her, too?

The little giraffe had just gone off exploring and she was quite safe.

"You're a naughty giraffe," scolded her mummy, but everyone was happy to see Jenny safe.

Puzzle play-time

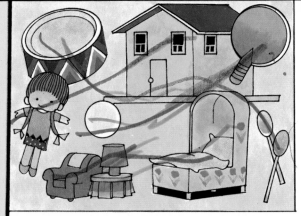

Match these items with their partners!

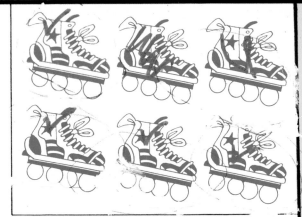

Which two skates are exactly the same?

Lead Katy through the maze to her doll.

Shade the dotted areas to "spring" a surprise!

Colour this picture with paints or crayons.

Princess Robyn

1 — Princess Robyn lives with her wicked uncle, King Jasper. Near Christmas, she *was* surprised to see "Santa" Jasper set off for Sherwood village with sacks.

2 — But Jasper hadn't had a change of heart. He wasn't *giving* presents, he was demanding them for himself. "Put them in my sack — or else," he ordered.

3 — Robyn was furious. Changing into her secret guise of the outlaw, Robin of the Woods, she visited the village carpenter, seeking a favour.

4 — On Christmas morning, a huge, gaily-wrapped present for Jasper appeared. He was too excited to notice Robin and the villagers watching him.

5 — Jasper ripped open the parcel and was delighted to find a new throne. "What a fitting gift," he gloated, "whoever it's from. Now, what does this lever do . . . ?"

6 — The king tugged at it and got a Christmas surprise he *hadn't* expected — a Jasper-in-the-box! To the cheers of all the villagers, he flew through the air . . .

7 — . . . and landed on top of the village Christmas tree! Princess Robyn returned the presents and a Merry Christmas was had by all — except Jasper!

My Baby Brother

"DECEMBER'S here again — just see!"
My brother heard me say.
"There's lots of things to do and make,
Before it's Christmas Day!"

Mum called out from the kitchen door,
"*I'm* making Christmas pud,
So come and have a stir and wish!"
It tasted *very* good!

One day, I said, "It's time to make
Our Christmas cards, you know."
We painted cheeky robins and
A snowman in the snow.

We caught a big red bus to town —
So many gifts to buy!
Ben brought his little trolley, and
We piled the presents high.

We hung up coloured paper chains
To make the room look jolly.
Then Dad brought home a great big bunch
Of scarlet-berried holly.

Some carollers came round to sing,
They crowded at the door.
We gave them each a fat mince pie —
And then they sang some more!

When it was Christmas Eve, we trimmed
Our prickly Christmas tree.
Then Benny hung his stocking up —
With one for Ted, you see.

And then, at last, came Christmas Day.
Ben gave me a great kiss.
We pulled a cracker and he laughed,
"A Happy Christmas, Sis!"

Penny Crayon

1 — When Penny Crayon went to join her friends sledging, she found some bullies throwing snowballs and spoiling their fun.

2 — One of the bullies took Dennis's sledge. "Hoi!" cried Dennis. "Bring that back!" Penny set to work with her magic crayons.

© PETER MADDOCKS 94

3 — Anything Penny drew with her magic crayons became real. Soon she had a huge sledge, pulled by a team of huskies.

4 — "Mush!" she called, and the huskies took off, scattering snow all over the bullies. "That's taught them!" grinned Dennis.

5 — Before long, however, the bullies were back, pelting snowballs at the snowman Penny had built.

6 — As fast as she could, Penny drew an *enormous* snowman! He came to life and terrified the bullies. "Help!" they shrieked, and ran off.

7 — "That's got rid of them," chuckled Penny. "Now for some fun!" Her chums pulled their sledges uphill, but . . .

8 — . . . the big snowman was sad. *He* didn't have a sledge! Penny's crayons fixed that, and *everyone* was happy!

You can colour this picture.

Witch *Winkle*

1 — Wendy Wilson has a most unusual chum — Winkle, a 300-year-old witch who lives in her attic. Winkle loves to help . . . even though not all her plans work out!

2 — The friendly witch was feeling very happy as she flew home on Christmas Eve. "I *am* looking forward to Santa's visit," she chuckled. "I wonder what he'll bring?"

3 — Wendy was in a bad mood, however. She was worried about her chimney. It was *filthy* ! "We can't expect Santa to come down *that* ," she sighed.

4 — When Wendy was asleep, Winkle crept downstairs. With a wave of her wand, she sent her broomstick shooting up the chimney. "*That'll* clean it," she smiled.

5 — But seconds later, there was a terrible howl from up the chimney. "I've never heard soot scream before," frowned the puzzled witch.

6 — Winkle climbed through the skylight to recover her broomstick, and who should she find there but a dazed and dirty *Santa* ! "Oops," gulped Winkle. "My broomstick's knocked him out of the chimney."

7 — Winkle was determined to make up to Santa. First, she gave him Dad's old dressing-gown. "It's — er — *different*, but at least it's clean," he muttered.

8 — "And I'll *keep* it clean," beamed Winkle, who waved her wand again and chanted, *"Brooms come forth and earn your keep, Santa needs a good, clean sweep!"*

9 — The broomsticks flew to all the other chimneys in town and began sweeping them clean. Santa *was* grateful. "I *hate* going down dirty chimneys," he admitted.

10 — Before long, the chimneys were spotless and Santa was able to set off once more. "I won't forget your kindness," he told Winkle. "You'll have an *extra* surprise tomorrow."

11 — Sure enough, as everyone was opening their presents on Christmas morning, there was a knock at the door. "Who's that?" asked Wendy.

12 — It was a *special* delivery, with a *special* gift — a Santa Claus dressing gown! "But who is it from?" gasped Dad. "This is a mystery!" "Not to me," chuckled Winkle to Wendy. "I'll explain later!"

Miranda's mirror

ONE morning, Miranda, the pretty fashion doll, found a small mirror on the floor in Julie's playroom.

"What's this?" she exclaimed.

Miranda had never seen a mirror before. She picked it up for a better look. She held it at arm's length and was so surprised, she nearly dropped it.

"I can't believe it!" exclaimed Miranda. "It's a picture of me!"

She called to her puppet friend, Mr Punch, "Come and look at this."

Mr Punch obviously did not know any better than Miranda. He stared into the mirror and shook his head.

"It's nothing like you!" he said disgustedly. "This is a picture of an ugly old man with a big nose, which has a red spot on the end of it."

Soon, there was quite an argument in the playroom. Miranda's pretty face looked cross and stubborn, which was most unlike her. She asked the soldier doll for his opinion, but he wasn't interested.

"I'm going on patrol around the playroom," he said.

2 — Finally, she snatched the mirror back from Mr Punch and pushed it into a drawer.

"It's a picture of me and I'm going to keep it!" she declared.

Next day, Miranda opened the drawer and let out a shriek, "Someone's stolen my picture! It's gone, it's gone!"

3 — All the toys helped to look for it, except for the little soldier, who was too busy making a farmyard.

"I do wish you would all stop rushing about!" sighed the soldier.

He put some tiny toy ducks on his pretend duck pond. He was so pleased he had found it in a drawer. You can guess what it was, of course. It was the lost mirror!

Just then, Miranda noticed the little pond.

"That's my picture!" she screamed and moved to pick it up.

But in her hurry, she slipped and stepped on the mirror. It broke into a hundred pieces.

At that very moment, they heard Julie opening the door and had to keep still.

"Why do you look so sad?" Julie asked Miranda brightly.

She set about cheering up her dolly by brushing her hair.

"Now I'll show you what you look like," said Julie.

She searched the room for her little mirror and soon found it.

"What a pity," she said as she caught sight of it in pieces. "I wonder how that happened? Never mind, I have another mirror."

4 — She returned with a much larger one.

"Look in the mirror. Aren't you smart?"

Miranda, Mr Punch and the rest of the toys stared in amazement. They could all see into the mirror which showed their reflections clearly. Now they understood and they started to see the funny side.

"I'm so sorry that I was cross with you all," said Miranda when Julie left the room.

Everyone forgave her — even the soldier!

Buzzy

I want to go to that!

FANCY DRESS CONTEST 2:15 TODAY

Oops — I've no time to make a costume.

I know what I'll do!

Everything I need is *here*.

Buzzy found all the things in the garden that she needed to make a clown costume! Can *you* see what she used?

Like it?

I've won first prize! Yippeee!

FIRST

Polly

1 — Polly was helping Rodney Reindeer to choose paint for his bedroom ceiling. "It's so cheap!" said Rodney. "It doesn't tell you what colour's inside," said Polly.

2 — Back home, when the friends opened the tin, they were in for a surprise. "It's navy blue!" gasped Polly. "I don't mind a bit," said Rodney. "I like navy blue."

3 — Soon the ceiling was finished, and even Rodney admitted it was too dark. "We tried to tell you navy blue was no use, but you wouldn't listen," said his friends.

4 — Kind-hearted Polly couldn't bear her friend to be unhappy, so, using scissors and silver foil, she thought of a way to cheer him up. The others *were* puzzled!

5 — While the others waited outside, Polly worked away in Rodney's bedroom. At last, she told them they could come in and see what she had been doing.

6 — Polly had stuck silver moons and stars all over the bedroom ceiling. "It's wonderful, just like the sky at night! Thank you, Polly," said Rodney.

Jean Genie

Gemma Jones discovered that if she slapped the back pocket of her jeans, she summoned her very own genie. Slaphappy, the genie, made Gemma's wishes come true.

1 — Gemma and her friend, Susan, were admiring cuddly toys in a shop window. "I wish I knew how to make them," sighed Gemma, and she slapped her back pocket.

2 — At once, Gemma's genie appeared. "Your wish is my command!" he grinned. "Jump on to my magic carpet and we'll fly to a toy factory." "Yippee!" yelled the girls.

3 — After sailing through the air for some time, Susan spotted the toy factory. "There it is, Slaphappy!" she cried to the genie. "Let's zoom down!" The doorman was amazed.

4 — He still looked stunned when Gemma and Susan arrived at the entrance. "Can we see the toys being made, please?" Gemma asked. "Visitors welcome — even you!" he replied.

5 — Inside the factory, the girls watched with interest as toy bunnies travelling along a conveyor belt had ears and bobtails fixed to them. "Oh, how sweet," smiled Gemma.

6 — Just then, however, Susan touched a lever and everything went wrong! "Oh, look what I've done," she gasped. The machine was sewing heads and tails in all the wrong places.

7 — Gemma quickly slapped her back pocket to call Slaphappy. "Make them like rabbits again!" she begged. But the silly genie thought she said "*live* rabbits!"

8 — Slaphappy snapped his fingers and the headless rabbits hopped *everywhere*! Next, the flustered genie conjured up two sheepdogs to round up the runaway rabbits.

9 — "Now we've got *double* trouble," groaned Gemma, closing her eyes. "Er . . . *triple* trouble, actually," sighed Susan as the factory manager approached, *hopping* mad.

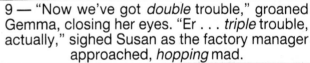

10 — He ordered the girls *and* the genie to start stitching heads, tails and ears on to all the bunnies. Slaphappy was about to joke "Heads or tails . . ." but he set to work instead.

11 — "Who said a stitch in time saves nine?" he muttered at the end of the day. He cheered up, however, when the manager let them go, giving the girls a gift of a bunny each!

There are lots of different animals in this picture. How many rabbits can you see? How many mice? How many squirrels? How many hedgehogs?

When you've finished counting the woodland animals, colour the picture with your paints.

Which two juggling mice are exactly the same?

Rearrange the letters above to find the names of the woodland shadow shapes.

Trace along the tangled paths to find which hedgehog finishes the race.

Can you find six differences between these two pictures?

Fairy Fay

1 — Fairy Fay and her friends had been busy for days, preparing a party for the fairy children. It was to be held that evening on board a boat on the lake.

2 — Peter Pixie fitted lovely coloured lights all round the deck and masts. "You've made a super job," smiled Fay. "We'll be able to play games on deck."

3 — It was very cold by the time the party was about to begin. "Wrap up warmly," said Fay. "It will be chilly as we row across the lake to the boat."

4 — When they reached the jetty, they were in for a shock. The lake had frozen solid! "What shall we do?" asked Eddie Elf. "We can't row over there now!"

5 — "We'll have to go home again," said Fay. The youngsters looked very disappointed. "Does that mean the party is cancelled?" they cried.

6 — But clever Fairy Fay had other ideas. "I want you all to fetch your ice skates," she explained. "We'll *skate* across!" Everyone immediately cheered up.

7 — "Right, get your skates on!" chuckled Fay when all the children were ready. "Let the party begin!" What fun they had together.

8 — Some of the fairies skated round the boat while the others climbed on board for hot mugs of cocoa. "This is a n-ice party!" joked Eddie.

Hetty "Hare"-dresser

RITA RABBIT ran a hairdressing shop for all the animals who lived in Dingle Dell.

One day, when Rita had to go into town on an errand, she asked her friend, Hetty Hare, to keep an eye on the shop for her.

"You needn't worry," Rita told her. "I haven't had any customers for days, so you'll have nothing to do."

2 — After a while, however, Hetty found doing nothing was very boring, so she decided to make herself useful.

"I've always wanted to try hairdressing," she chuckled to herself. "It can't be too difficult, and I've watched Rita lots of times."

Carefully, she wrote out a "Special Offer" notice board, put up an "Open" sign and told her friends to spread the news round the village.

"Let everyone know that Hetty the hairdresser's is now open for business," she said.

3 — Hetty's first customer was Mrs Squirrel.

"I had no idea you were a hairdresser, Hetty," she said, "but I must say, your prices are most reasonable."

"Oh, I can do all sorts of things," said Hetty. "Er — what would you like me to do for you today, Mrs Squirrel?"

"Just a trim, please, Hetty, and you can tidy up my tail while you're at it," said Mrs Squirrel.

"One tidy tail coming up," said Hetty, and she began applying all the lotions she could find.

4 — But, oh dear, when Hetty had finished, Mrs Squirrel looked round and let out a shriek of alarm. Her tail was now a very bright, curly blue!

"This is terrible!" shrieked Mrs Squirrel. "I look a freak! Whoever heard of a squirrel with a blue tail! I shall be having words with Miss Rita Rabbit about this when she returns," said Mrs Squirrel, as she stomped out of the shop.

However, no sooner had Mrs Squirrel gone huffily on her way when some of the young animals of Dingle Dell came running up.

5 — "Would you please do *our* hair, Hetty?" they asked. "We saw what you did with Mrs Squirrel's tail and we think her blue tail is neat, really neat!"

"Oh, this is a surprise," cried Hetty, but she set to work, cutting and colouring.

When Rita arrived back at the shop, she was astonished to see so many happy and *colourful* customers!

"I must leave you in charge more often, Hetty," she laughed.

Christmas crossword

To decorate the Christmas tree, you must first find your way through the maze. As you go, write the names of the objects you come across in the crossword till the tree is full.

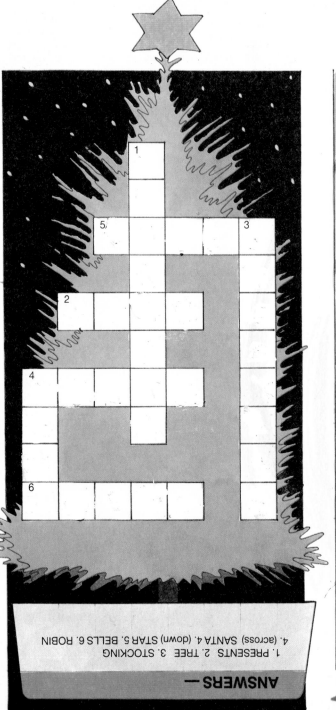

1 down

3 down

2 across

5 across

4 down

6 across

4 across

The School under the sea

MARIGOLD the mermaid had been ill for a long time.

"I must have missed a lot of schoolwork," she sighed.

Professor Dolphin, the schoolmaster, went to visit Marigold.

"I'm going to try to help you to catch up on your work," he told Marigold kindly.

He sent a shoal of pretty little fish to Marigold's grotto, and, when they arranged themselves in rows adding up to seven, Marigold clapped her hands with glee.

"You're helping me with my sums!" she gasped. "I never remember my sevens."

Soon, Marigold knew all the numbers that could join together to make seven.

2 — Professor Dolphin was so pleased with his experiment he sent along Olivia Octopus next. Olivia coiled her tentacles then pulled out letters until she spelled the word "Marigold."

"You're spelling my name!" cried Marigold delightedly. "Have you come to help with my spelling?"

Olivia held up letters to answer "yes," then she showed eight words at a time to make a sentence. Soon, Marigold's reading had improved greatly.

Once again, Professor Dolphin was pleased with Marigold's progress.

"That's the spelling and sums sorted out," he thought. "Now for the writing."

3 — This time, he sent along Sammy Swordfish who made Marigold chuckle by diving nose down into the sandy sea bed and wriggling along to make all sorts of silly-looking squiggles.

"Why don't you guide me, Marigold?" he said after a while. "Let's see what pretty letters we can make in the sand."

So Marigold held on to Sammy's tail and directed his sharp nose into the sand.

"You are just like a giant pencil," chuckled the little mermaid. "It's fun to write like this!"

Marigold was so happy playing with Sammy that she didn't realise that she was really practising her writing.

4 — The clever swordfish thought of lots of different games to make Marigold write in the sand.

"We'll play copycats now," Sammy said smiling. "You must copy everything I write."

And he wrote "Clever Sammy" in the sand. Marigold carefully copied the writing then, laughingly, she wrote "Brilliant Marigold."

"Now *you* must copy what I've written," she told Sammy.

With Sammy's help, Marigold soon caught up with her writing.

Professor Dolphin *was* pleased.

5 — But then, something else happened to make Marigold unhappy. Sports Day was coming up and Marigold *loved* sports.

When Doctor Walrus came to examine her, however, he said she was well enough to go along and watch the sports, but that she mustn't take part.

"Oh, please let me enter the Swimming Race," begged Marigold, but Doctor Walrus said, "Definitely not. You are not strong enough."

The little mermaid buried her head in her bed and cried.

"But I feel so much better," she sobbed.

6 — Professor Dolphin didn't like to see the little mermaid so sad.

"Poor Marigold," he sighed. "What can I do to help her be happy again? There must be *something* she can enter without swimming or diving — but what?"

The professor pondered for a long time.

"There's the Deepest Diver competition, the Swimming Race, the Treasure Hunt, the Shell Searcher competition . . ." Professor Dolphin muttered as he went through the sports day programme.

Then he remembered the Prettiest Sea Horse competition, and he smiled.

"Now *that* gives me an idea," he grinned.

He was so pleased that he skipped with the merchildren before joyously setting off.

When he returned, Professor Dolphin was leading a team of sea horses.

"This year," he announced, "we are going to have a *new* event. It will be a Sea Horse Race and," he hesitated, "Doctor Walrus has agreed that Marigold can take part!"

"Hooray!" cheered the merchildren.

7 — The little mermaid won the race easily and then she was given good news.

"You can go back to school next term," decided Doctor Walrus.

"But the other merchildren will have to work *extra* hard to keep up with *you* now," laughed Professor Dolphin.

Birthdays to

January — Carnation	July — Larkspur
IQN	

February — Violet	August — Gladiolus

March — Daffodil	September — Aster

April — Sweet Pea	October — Calendula

May — Lily of the Valley	November — Chrysanthemum

June — Rose	December — Narcissus

Don't forget your family and friends' birthdays, girls. Write them in the birthday planner above. There's even a special flower for every month.

Remember.

Get ahead — get a hat!

Make a party hat by drawing a circle on thin card. Cut out the circle and then cut a section, as shown, from the circle. Tape the sides of the section together to fit your head. Add a design.

Nice 'n' simple

Fold a piece of card in half, stick on tissue paper petals in a flower shape and draw on a stem to make a nice and simple birthday card. Write your greeting inside.

Pop a surprise!

Give someone a surprise card. Fold a 5 cm wide strip of thick paper into a concertina. Draw a funny face, stick it to the concertina and then stick the other concertina end inside the card. Flatten the concertina to close the card and, when it opens, out pops the surprise!

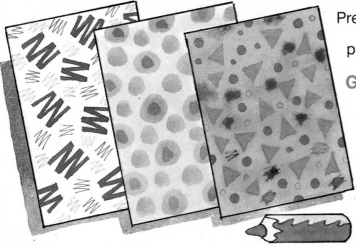

Pretty patterns on plain paper make nice **Gift Wrap!**

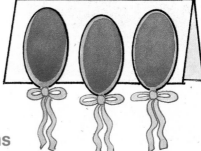

Invitations

Party invitations can be made by putting bold balloon shapes on the front of folded card and adding ribbons.

Tina's magic toybox

1 — The pantomime, Cinderella, was being shown at the local theatre. Mummy and Daddy took Tina along to see it. "Poor little Cinders," said Tina when the ugly sisters were unkind to her.

2 — Tina enjoyed her outing — and there was another treat in store for her next morning. "I'm invited to a fancy dress party," smiled Tina.

3 — "I can go as the ragged Cinders," said Tina. "I've got the right outfit for that." On the day of the party, Tina put on her costume. Then she looked for shoes.

4 — But none of her shoes looked right. "I can't go barefoot like Cinders did!" she thought. "Let's see what's in my magic toybox." The little girl found a pair of sparkling slippers.

5 — Tina tried them on. "They're too fancy," she sighed. But then, the magic took over and Tina found herself wearing a beautiful ballgown!

6 — Just like Cinders, Tina became the lovely Cinderella. "Wow!" gasped her chums. "Your costume is *magic*!" How right they were!

Patty and the Grisly Gripe

FAR on the other side of a great forest, lay a sad town called Down-in-the-Dumps. It was sad because the terrible giant, Grisly Gripe, wouldn't let anyone make a single sound.

No one ever laughed or sang, the children never played, and the dogs never barked. Even the mice wore slippers to cross the street, so the giant would not hear them!

"If I should hear the slightest sigh,
I'll want to know the reason why!"
the Gripe growled.

Grisly Gripe was so big and so ugly that no one ever dared cross him. He had great sharp teeth, and huge, red ears that could hear the smallest noise.

"No chatter of children, no tweet of a bird,
No rattle or prattle at all must be heard!"
he boomed from his cave in the mountain.

The Gripe hated giggling, because it gave him a headache. He hated singing, and even made the Town Hall clock stop its happy chime.

"Why can't we have fun?" Patty, a little girl who lived in the town, asked her daddy. "It's Christmas Eve and I've never had a Christmas party."

Patty's daddy sighed.

"Because the Grisly Gripe won't let us have any fun," he replied.

"But *why* ?" Patty asked again.

"Because he doesn't like to see anyone happy — and he's so big that everyone is afraid of him," her daddy told her.

"Then," said Patty sadly, "I can't see that we'll ever be happy again."

That night, Patty looked out her bedroom window and started to cry.

"I wish we could have Christmas like everyone else," she sobbed.

Suddenly, Patty saw a bright star twinkling above the little town. Then, with a *swoosh,* the star skimmed across the sky and fairy dust fell to the ground.

Patty could hardly believe what she saw. There, in the Town Square, was the largest Christmas cracker she had ever seen!

"A magic cracker! That must have been a *wishing* star!" Patty cheered.

She ran into the street.

"Come and see the magic cracker!" she called to everyone.

Windows opened and sleepy heads peeked out.

"A giant cracker!" they gasped.

People rushed from every door. They joined hands and danced and sang. They forgot about Grisly Gripe.

Then, suddenly, there was an enormous roar from the mountain.

"The Gripe!" everyone yelled in horror, suddenly remembering about the giant again! And they ran away.

"What's this, then?" the Gripe snorted when he saw the cracker.

He grabbed one end of the cracker and pulled.

"He's going to steal our magic cracker!" Patty gasped.

Before anyone could stop her, Patty rushed from her hiding place and grabbed the other end of the cracker.

When the people saw how brave the little girl was, they came out of their houses to help her. They hauled and heaved and pulled with Patty.

But, as the Gripe tugged once more, the cracker split with a huge *BANG* !

The Gripe tumbled over on to his back and the townspeople held their breath, wondering just how angry he would be.

He sat up with a roar but, as he looked around, a look of happy amazement passed over his face. For out of the magic cracker had spilled colourful balloons and streamers, silly hats and horns and lots and lots of gaily-wrapped presents. There was even one for the Gripe!

"For *me*?" he beamed. "No one has ever given me a present before."

And the Gripe was so pleased that he insisted on joining in the Christmas party.

"This is the best Christmas anyone could have," Patty laughed.

Everyone, including the Gripe, agreed, and the little town was never called Down-in-the-Dumps again!

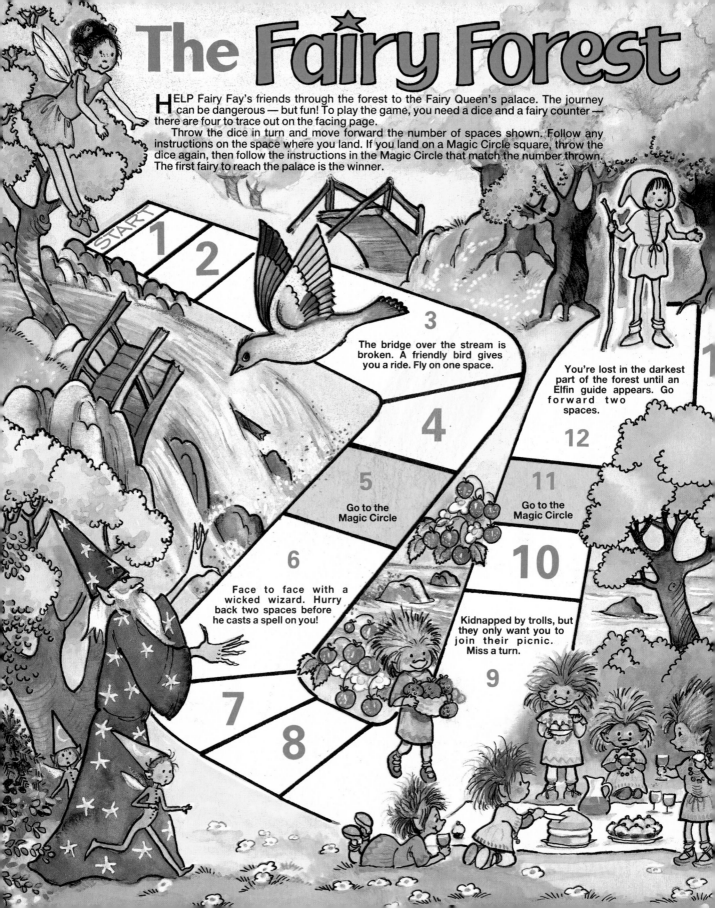

The Fairy Forest

HELP Fairy Fay's friends through the forest to the Fairy Queen's palace. The journey can be dangerous — but fun! To play the game, you need a dice and a fairy counter — there are four to trace out on the facing page.

Throw the dice in turn and move forward the number of spaces shown. Follow any instructions on the space where you land. If you land on a Magic Circle square, throw the dice again, then follow the instructions in the Magic Circle that match the number thrown. The first fairy to reach the palace is the winner.

START

1

2

3

The bridge over the stream is broken. A friendly bird gives you a ride. Fly on one space.

4

You're lost in the darkest part of the forest until an Elfin guide appears. Go forward two spaces.

12

5

Go to the Magic Circle

11

Go to the Magic Circle

6

Face to face with a wicked wizard. Hurry back two spaces before he casts a spell on you!

10

Kidnapped by trolls, but they only want you to join their picnic. Miss a turn.

9

7

8